This Book Belongs To :

Made in United States
Orlando, FL
21 April 2023

32321181R00063